THE
CALL
OF THE
WILD

a TREASURY OF ILLUSTRATED CLASSICS™

THE
CALL
OF THE
WILD

by
Jack London

**Abridged, adapted,
and illustrated**
by
quadrum■

Quadrum Solutions, Mumbai, India

Modern Publishing
A Division of Unisystems, Inc.
New York, New York 10022
Series UPC: 38170

Cover art by Pete Roberts

Contents

CHAPTER 1

Into the Wide Open

A long time ago, in 1897, under the sunny skies of Northern California, lived a happy and carefree dog called Buck. He lived with his owner, Judge Miller, in a beautiful house that stood away from the street, half hidden among the trees. A wide, cool veranda ran around the four sides of the house, which was approached by graveled driveways that wound about beautiful lawns and tall poplar trees.

The back garden of the house was even larger than the front. There were great stables and kennels, where Buck was

eyed enviously by the smaller dogs. Dozen of horses were tended to by stable boys. There were rows of vine-clad servants' cottages, several outhouses, green pastures, orchards, berry patches, and grape vines. There was also a pumping plant for a well, and a big cement tank where Judge Miller's boys took their morning plunge and kept cool in the hot afternoon.

The Call of the Wild

Buck shared this house with the judge's family and several other dogs. These included a couple of fox terriers who occupied the many kennels outdoors and Buck's friends Toots, a Japanese pug, and Ysabel, the Mexican hairless, who never set a foot outdoors. The terriers were always yelping at Toots and Ysabel, who had to be protected by the scores of housemaids armed with their brooms.

Neither house dog nor kennel dog, Buck was without doubt the judge's favorite. Buck's father, Elmo, a huge St. Bernard, had been the judge's inseparable companion and it was clear to everyone that Buck would follow his father's footsteps. Although not as large as his father, for his mother had been a Scotch shepherd, he weighed 140 pounds, enough to command universal respect. He had great pride in himself and always carried himself with dignity.

Buck spent his time playing outdoors, running, hunting, and swimming in the California sunshine. His favorite games included belly flopping into the pool with the judge's sons and early morning walks with Mollie and Alice, the judge's daughters. On cold winter evenings he would curl up at the judge's feet in front of the bright fireplace in the library. Oh, how Buck loved his wonderful life!

One evening, when the judge was away at a meeting of the Raisin Growers' Association and his sons were very busy organizing an athletic club, Manuel, the gardener, took Buck for a walk through the orchards. Buck did not notice anything out of the ordinary.

But Manuel was not just taking Buck out for a walk; he had far more evil intentions. Manuel was a gambler and had lost a lot of money as a result. He intended to steal Buck and sell him off.

Buck did not read the newspapers, or he would have known that trouble was brewing—not for him alone but for every strong, muscular dog with warm hair everywhere from Puget Sound to San Diego. Gold had been discovered in the Arctic region, and thousands of men were rushing into the Northland. These men needed dogs, particularly heavy dogs who could pull loaded sleds, and dogs with warm, furry coats to protect them from the subzero temperatures and the frost.

He walked Buck toward a little flag station called College Park, where he met a scruffy stranger. The gardener sold Buck to this strange man for hundred dollars.

"You should have wrapped up the goods before you brought him," the strange man said to Manuel.

Manuel doubled up a rope and tied it around Buck's neck, under his collar. Although Buck was surprised, he

The Call of the Wild

accepted it, for that is what he had been
trained to do: to trust the men he knew.
But when the rope was handed over to the
strange man, Buck growled menacingly.
The man tightened the rope, and to his

surprise, Buck began to choke. As the man tightened the rope mercilessly, Buck felt his strength disappear and he passed out.

Before he knew what had happened, Buck found himself bundled in the baggage car of a train with the stranger. As the train began to move, Buck became confused and began thrashing about in anger. His restless sounds were heard by a concerned baggage handler, but the stranger pretended that Buck was his friend and made up a fake story. "I'm taking him to San Francisco to a doctor," he lied.

Never in his life had he been treated so badly, and never in all his life had he been so angry. But he felt his strength disappear, and his eyes became glazed. The man at the train station sold him to someone else. Finally, cramped inside a wooden crate, he was deposited into another train. Two days and two nights later he arrived in Seattle, tired, hungry, and lost.

At the station, a large man in a red sweater signed the book for the driver and took delivery of Buck. But now, Buck had changed—he was no longer the carefree dog he had once been. Hunger and exhaustion had made him very angry and ferocious.

The man in the red sweater took Buck to a place where there were many other dogs locked up in crates. In his cage Buck was snarling and growling, rushing at the wood, sinking his teeth into it, wrestling with it. As soon as he was let out, he launched at the man with all his weight. But midair, the man struck him with a club. This was the first time Buck had ever been hit with a club. Each time he charged at the man, he was struck. Finally, he lay sprawled on the floor, blood-soaked and senseless. Buck had learned his lesson for life: that he stood no chance against a man with a club.

Now and again men came and bought one or more of the dogs. Buck wondered where the dogs went and why they didn't come back. He also became afraid for his own future and was glad each time he wasn't selected.

Yet one day, a French-Canadian man named Perrault walked in and began talking to the man in the red sweater. When he saw Buck he recognized straight away that he was special. "He's one in a thousand," Perrault said, and bought Buck for three hundred dollars. He also bought Curly, a good-natured Newfoundland, and led them away from the man in the red sweater.

Perrault was joined by his friend Francois, who was also a French-Canadian, and the two men led the two dogs aboard a boat called the *Narwhal*. As the boat pulled away, Buck and Curly stood on the deck and looked at the receding Seattle shore. It was the last they were to see of the warm Southland—for Alaska was the boat's destination.

Onboard the *Narwhal*, Buck and Curly met two other dogs. One was named Dave, who wasn't the least bit friendly and preferred to be left alone. Even when Curly and Buck became excited and afraid when the *Narwhal* crossed the Queen Charlotte Sound and tossed about, Dave barely raised his head, gave a bored yawn, and went straight back to sleep.

The other dog was a big, snow-white chap from Spitzbergen named Spitz. He was friendly, but in a cunning way. At Buck's first meal on the boat Spitz tried to steal his food. But before Buck could punish him, Spitz was punished by Francois. It was after this incident that Buck began to respect Francois.

Days and nights passed, and the *Narwhal* continued to plod along. It became apparent to Buck that with each passing day the weather became steadily colder. At last, one morning, the propeller was quiet and the *Narwhal* was bursting with excitement. Everybody felt it, including the dogs.

Francois unleashed the dogs and brought them up to the deck. As Buck took his first step on the surface of this new land, his feet sank into soft white mush. He sprang back in surprise. More of this flaky white stuff was falling around him through the air. He shook himself, but more fell upon him. It felt cold on his nose as he licked it. It bit like fire, but was gone in a minute. He sniffed it and tried again, but with the same result.

Everybody around him laughed out loud, and though Buck was ashamed that he did not know better, he was excited— after all, this was first snow, the first experience of his new life.

CHAPTER 2

Buck's New Companions

Upon landing in Dyea Beach, Alaska, Buck realized his new life would be nothing like his carefree life in California. Every hour brought to him a new shock and surprise. He felt as if he had been pulled out of civilization and thrust into the primitive.

His owners, Perrault and Francois, worked for the Canadian government as couriers and Buck's work was to help them deliver important despatches. Buck wasn't used to being a work dog but he accepted his task wisely and did his best, although it

The Call of the Wild

was all new and strange to him. Although his dignity was sorely hurt by being made to work as a draft animal, he was too wise to rebel. He quietly accepted the many straps and buckles that were placed upon him when he was put to work on his very first day hauling Francois on a sled to the forest, returning with a load of firewood.

Here, there was no loafing around in the sun; there was neither peace nor safety. Buck knew that he must be constantly alert

for these men and the dogs weren't like those in his life back home. There were many other dogs in this new land, but they were unlike his earlier friends Toots and Ysabel. A shocking experience that would haunt him for a long time afterward made him see that these dogs were not town dogs, but savages who fought like wolves.

It was their first day in Dyea Beach and Perrault and Francois set up camp not

far from a log store. Curly, in her usual friendly manner, bounded up to a husky dog who, being the size of a fully grown wolf, was much smaller than Curly. But all of a sudden, with no warning at all, like a leap in the flash, he leaped up and bit Curly in the face. Although larger, Curly proved to be no match for the fierce beast.

It was the wolf manner of fighting, to strike and leap away, but this was something else. Before long, thirty or forty huskies had arrived and Curly was quickly outnumbered. She tried to meet her opponent, who struck her again and leaped away. When she rushed at him again, she met with his chest and was tumbled off her feet. She never regained herself. The circle closed in upon her, snarling and yelping, and she was buried, screaming with agony.

When Francois and Perrault realized what was happening, they rushed to the scene of the fight with clubs and shooed

off the dogs within minutes, but it was too late. Curly had already lost her life.

Buck was shocked by the sudden and unexpected loss of his friend, which took place right in front of his eyes. He knew then that there was no fair play in this new place. Once down, that was the end of you. He decided that he would make

The Call of the Wild

sure that he was always careful and that he would never let anything get the better of him.

He saw Spitz run out his tongue and laugh at the sight of Curly being mauled by the huskies. From that moment on, Buck hated him with a deathless hatred.

While Buck was still mourning the loss of his friend, Perrault was eager to get on with business. Francois and Perrault introduced two new additions to their little team. The two new huskies were brothers, but were as different as day and night. While Billee was extremely good-natured, his brother Joe was the exact opposite— always sulking.

Buck was happy to see them and greeted them warmly, hoping to become friends. Dave, as expected, ignored both completely. Spitz did exactly what he had done with Buck: He tried to bully them.

The Call of the Wild

Billee responded to all three by wagging his tail in appreciation, but when he saw that friendlessness wasn't working, he ran off. Spitz got to him, anyway, and bit him hard on his side. But Joe would not be intimidated by Spitz. When Spitz circled around him, Joe turned around to face him, snarling and snapping. So terrible was Joe's appearance that even Spitz knew that he had to back down. So to cover his own discomfort, he turned his attention back to harmless Billee and proceeded to drive him to the confines of the camp.

Not too long after, there was yet another new face. A long, lean, and thin husky called Sol-leks, which meant "the Angry One." With a battle-scarred face and one blind eye, so commanding was his presence that even Spitz did not have the courage to mess with Sol-leks and decided to leave him alone.

Sol-leks did have one peculiarity, as Buck discovered the hard way. He did not like to be approached on his blind side. Unknowingly, Buck committed exactly this blunder. Annoyed, Sol-leks attacked Buck and caused a deep slash on his shoulder. It was a lesson Buck learned for life and till the end of their friendship he avoided Sol-leks's blind side and never had any more trouble from him.

Sol-leks, like Dave, was aloof and wanted to be left alone. But as Buck would discover soon, both dogs shared one more thing in common.

In time, three more huskies were added to the team. They were finally a team of nine—strong, eager, and alert. Each dog had a place of his own. Dave was the wheeler or sled dog; pulling in front of him was Buck; then Sol-leks; and finally the rest of the team leading single file to the leader, a position filled by Spitz.

Before long, the team was on their way to Dyea Canon. Buck was glad to be going and although the work was hard, he found that he did not particularly despise it. He was surprised by the eagerness of the other dogs and which was communicated to him; but still more surprised by the change in Dave and Sol-leks. They were like new dogs, completely transformed by the harness. All passiveness and unconcern had disappeared—they were alert and active, anxious that the work should go well, and irritable with whatever, by delay or confusion, slowed down that work. The toil of the traces seemed to be the very purpose of their existence and it was all that they lived for and the only thing in which they took delight.

Buck was intentionally placed between Sol-leks and Dave so that he could learn from them. While Buck proved to be a good student, both dogs proved to be more than generous teachers. They made sure that he did not make too many mistakes, and were sure to nip him with their teeth if he did. Once, during a brief halt, when he got tangled in the traces and delayed the start, both Dave and Sol-leks flew at him and administered a good beating. The

resulting tangle was even worse, but Buck took good care to keep the traces clear thereafter. But both Dave and Sol-leks were just, never nipping him unfairly or without reason.

Buck learned quickly—he learned that he must stop at the command of "ho" and to go ahead at the command of "mush." He soon knew that he must swing wide on the bends and that he must keep clear of the wheeler when a loaded shed shot downhill. Soon the nagging stopped completely. Francois's whip snapped less, and Perrault even honored Buck by lifting up his feet and carefully examining them.

Only Spitz seized a chance to snap at Buck whenever he had the opportunity, but Perrault and Francois were happy enough with Buck's work. They performed an important job for the Canadian government and were keen to have the best dogs they could—and both were particularly happy with Buck's progress. As a rule, Perrault traveled ahead of the team of dogs, plodding along the snow with webbed shoes to make it easier for them. Francois guided the sled. Sometimes the two men exchanged places, but not often. Perrault was in a hurry, and he prided himself on his knowledge of ice—which was indispensable, for the fall ice was very thin, and where there was swift water, there was no ice at all.

Day after day, Buck toiled in the traces with the other dogs. But pulling a sled was only one of the many things that Buck would have to learn in order to survive in his new life. As time would prove, Buck had many lessons to learn, including some that weren't pleasant.

CHAPTER 3

Learning New Tricks

As night covered Dyea Beach, Buck found it hard to fall asleep. It was his first night in the extreme conditions of the Northland and he was freezing. A chilly wind went straight to his bones, stinging the wound on his shoulder. He tried to sleep on the snow, but the frost drove him shivering up to his feet. He was drawn to the dim glow of the candle that illuminated Perrault and Francois's tent. Buck thought about the wintry evenings he would spend curled up with the judge in front of the library fire. He assumed

37

that he could enter the tent and look for some warmth.

But Perrault and Francois had other ideas going on and, cursing Buck, they threw him out, bombarding him with cooking utensils. He tried to sleep outside on the white blanket of snow, but the frost brought him up on his feet again. Buck walked around the other tents, looking for somewhere to sleep, but had no luck. Occasionally some savage dogs tried to attack him, but he had learned fast and he snarled at them ferociously and they left him alone.

He walked around looking for a spot to get comfortable when he realized that he couldn't find any of the other dogs. Again he wandered through the camp, looking for them, but they all seemed to have disappeared.

"Do they know something I don't?"

he wondered. He wandered through the camp in search of someone who could advise him on how he could get through the night. He wondered if the others had been allowed in the tent. But he believed Francois and Perrault to be just and he saw no reason why they would allow the other dogs into the tent and yet throw him out. Confused and desolate, he began circling the tent, when suddenly the snow gave away from under his feet and he sank down into the ground.

He yelped in surprise when he felt something wriggling under his feet. Afraid, he sprang back and started snarling. But a friendly little yelp reassured him, and he returned to the hole to investigate. The warm air filled his nostrils, and there he saw, curled up under the snow, Billee sleeping snug as a little ball.

He whined and wriggled his apology to Billee, who, sweet-natured as ever, gave

The Call of the Wild

Buck's face a warm, wet lick.

"So that's how they do it," Buck thought, and walked off quickly, eager to try this new trick for himself. He carefully selected a spot and then dug a hole for himself. Within moments the heat from his body had filled up the hole and he fell asleep almost instantly. It had been a long and difficult day, and he was exhausted.

He remained fast asleep until he was awoken by the sounds of the camp springing to life in the morning. At first he was disoriented, not knowing where he was and what he was doing in this strange, cold place. It had snowed during the night and the hole he had dug for himself was buried. Fear filled his being, and he darted out of the hole. The snow fell all around him, and he suddenly remembered everything—the nightmare that had begun with a stroll with the gardener.

But the team had a hard day's run

ahead of them. They would run deep in the lonely North, down lakes that filled the craters of extinct volcanoes. At the end of the day they pulled into a camp at the head of Lake Bennett, where hundreds of gold seekers were building boats.

Each day they would leave at the crack of dawn and would pull into the camp at dark. Buck and the team worked harder and harder every day, crawling into their holes during night to sleep. Every evening each dog was given a pound of sun-dried salmon as his dinner; Buck, being a larger dog, was given a pound and a half of the fish. But it was never enough, and he suffered from perpetual hunger pangs. Yet the other dogs, because they weighed less and were born to this life, managed to keep in good condition.

Buck also had to quickly abandon his California eating habits. As a domestic dog, he ate slowly, taking his time and enjoying his meal. But in the Northland, his companions always finished before him and then rushed toward him to steal his food. As he fought off one or more thieves, his food was inevitably stolen by another dog. So he learned to eat quickly.

Hunger also compelled him to steal. He once watched Pike, one of the other dogs, steal a slice of bacon from Perrault when his back was turned, and Buck did exactly the same himself. There was an uproar in the camp, but luckily he wasn't suspected. Dub, an awkward blunderer, who was always getting caught, was punished for Buck's misdeed.

But this was so much more than just theft; the act marked Buck's adaptability, his capacity to adjust himself to changing conditions, the lack of which would have meant swift and terrible death. But the decay of morals was not the only thing that had changed. In this new life, morals were

The Call of the Wild

a handicap. They had been important in the Southland, which was governed under the law of love and fellowship, to respect private property and personal feelings; but in the Northland, under the law of club and fang, those who considered such things important were fools and Buck knew now that as long as he held on to his morals, he would not prosper. In his civilized life, he would have died for his morals, but now his survival was more important than defending his morals. In short, he did the things he did because it was easier to do them than not.

Buck did not try to reason this out— he was fit, that was all, and unconsciously he accommodated himself to the new way of life.

He had begun to look the part. His muscles became hard as iron, and he became oblivious to ordinary pain. His body learned to accept any food that it was given, and his senses of sight and sound became acute. He could tell in his sleep if a sound meant peace or danger. He could bite the ice collected between his toes with his teeth. He could now scent the wind and forecast a night in advance.

But it was not merely experience that had changed Buck. Recent events had awoken instincts that had been dead for generations. He remembered back to the time when wild dogs lived in packs, hunting their food. Domestication had made his breed forget their ancestors. But for Buck, the old survival instincts returned without effort or discovery, and under the fierce conditions that he faced they only grew stronger and stronger with each passing day.

In many ways he remembered back to the early days of the breed, to the time when the wild dogs roamed in packs

through the wild forest and killed their meat as they ran it down. It wasn't difficult for Buck to learn to fight and hunt in the wolf way, like his ancestors. This stirred the old life within him, and the old tricks that were part of his heredity became his tricks.

So when he pointed his nose up to the moon and howled like a wolf, it was as if his ancestors were howling through him. The song he sang was their song, a song of sadness and what the cold and the dark meant to them.

CHAPTER 4

The Attack of the Huskies

The growth of the primitive beast in Buck continued as time passed, but it was a silent and secret growth. Now he was clearly cunning, poised, and in control. With time, he came to terms with his new life. But he was still too busy adjusting to his new environment to feel at ease. He made sure that he did not pick fights with any of his new mates; he went out of his way to avoid fights whenever possible.

But the relationship between Buck and Spitz did not improve at all, and the

bitter hatred between the two kept getting worse. At first, on the *Narwhal*, Buck had ignored Spitz most of the time, but he had hated him from the minute he saw Spitz smile at Curly's death. Despite his feelings, Buck kept out of Spitz's way. He was not a rash dog and did not prompt any fights. He showed no impatience with the other dog, choosing instead to ignore him. Spitz saw in Buck a capable rival and went out of his way to bully Buck and was always looking for a fight, which would end in the death of one of them.

This fight would have taken place early on in their trip had it not been for an unexpected incident. It came one evening when the team had settled into their camp after a day of very hard work. Heavy snow, a biting wind, and a deep darkness made it difficult for them to find a decent camp site. Perrault and Francois were forced to make their bed on the ice of the lake, as they had discarded their tent to travel light. They managed to light a fire with some driftwood, but it thawed through the ice and they were forced to eat their dinner in the dark.

Buck found a sheltering rock under which he made his nest. He was so snug and comfortable that he did not even want to leave it when Francois distributed their dinner. When Buck returned after his meal, he saw that someone had stolen his space. He knew that the trespasser would have been Spitz. Until then, Buck had avoided all confrontations with Spitz, but that day he was overcome with anger and strife and he sprang upon Spitz with unbridled fury.

This surprised both dogs equally, as Spitz's past experiences with Buck had taught him that Buck was a timid dog who held his own only because of his large

The Call of the Wild

size. Even both men were stunned. But Francois was clearly on Buck's side. "Give it to him, by God," he said. "Give it to the dirty thief."

This was the opportunity Spitz had been waiting for. Buck was equally prepared. The two dogs began circling, looking for the advantage, when they were interrupted by a shout from Perrault and

the loud slam of a club upon a bony body.

The unexpected had happened, and their battle for supremacy was postponed for some time in the future. The camp had been attacked by an army of forty or fifty starving huskies who had crept in while Buck and Spitz were fighting. Both men lunged at the huskies, but they fought back, sneering and biting, made crazy by the smell of the food. In one altercation, the food box capsized and all its contents spilled on the floor. The famished huskies fell upon the food and managed to devour it all under a shower of blows.

In the meanwhile the team dogs figured out what was happening and jumped out of their nests to fight side by side Francois and Perrault. But there was no opposing these starving huskies as they set upon the team. Buck had never seen such dogs—their bones were almost bursting through their skin. But they were terrifying

and unstoppable. At once Buck was attacked by three huskies and they ripped and slashed his head and shoulders. The other team dogs suffered a similar fate. Billee was crying, Joe was snapping like a dragon, and Dave and Sol-leks were bleeding from their many wounds while fighting side by side. Joe caught hold of one husky's foreleg and crunched it down to the bone, then Pike got hold of the crippled creature and broke his neck. Dub and Dolly, the new dogs, were also in the fight.

Buck responded quickly and got one adversary in the throat and was encouraged to throw himself with gusto at the others. Just then, he felt teeth sink into his own throat. It was Spitz, who took the chance to get back at Buck. Buck was shocked by this treacherous behavior, but wisely realized that it was not the right time to react.

Perrault and Francois rushed to help their sled dogs, having cleaned out their

The Call of the Wild

side of the camp. Afraid, the famished and crazy beasts rushed off the dogs and Buck managed to shake himself free. But it was only for a few moments. The men had to run back to save the food supplies, and the huskies returned to attack the dogs.

They fought as much as they could, but had to take flight in order to survive. Billee, terrified into bravery, struggled through the circle of savage dogs and ran across the ice. She was followed by Pike and Dub and then the rest of the team. As Buck collected himself to run behind them, he saw Spitz get ready to overthrow him. He braced himself to take the shock, and then followed the rest of the team.

Later, all the team dogs gathered together to take refuge in the forest. Battle weary, they were all a sorry sight. Each was injured in several places. Poor Joe had lost an eye, Dub was injured in a hind leg, Billee's ear was chewed to ribbons,

and Dolly had a badly torn throat.

When they returned to camp the next morning, they saw that the huskies had wrecked havoc. All the food had been eaten, and the huskies had even chewed on the sled lashings and canvas. They had even eaten a pair of Perrault's moose-hide moccasins and two feet of lash from the end of Francois's whip. In fact, nothing had escaped the famished huskies.

Francois was annoyed and upset at what had happened. After he had surveyed the damage, he took a moment to look at the wounded dogs.

"Do you think that these bites could cause madness in the dogs?" Francois asked. Perrault shook his head without conviction. He *was* afraid that the fight might cause madness among the dogs. The men were worried; they still had almost four hundred miles to complete and they could not afford to have any madness break out among their dogs. What they did not realize was that madness had already set in to one of the dogs.

But two hours and much exertion later, the men had somehow managed to put the harness into shape and the wounded team was back on its way to tackle the hardest part of their journey to Dawson, the hardest that they had ever tackled.

CHAPTER 5

The Trail to Dawson

There was still four hundred miles to cover to Dawson, and the team needed to make up for the lost time. They needed at first to tackle the Thirty-Mile River, which was wide open, and the ice was dangerous. It took them six days to cover those terrible thirty miles. It was the hardest trail they had ever encountered, and each one of those miles was accomplished at great risk to both man and dog.

A dozen times Perrault, nosing the way, broke through the ice bridges, saved each time by the long pole he held in such

a way that it fell across the hole made by his body when he fell. But the temperature was fifty below zero, and each time he fell he had to build a fire and dry his clothes. But Perrault was fearless and soldiered on bravely. It was precisely for these qualities that he was picked to be a government courier. He did not hesitate in taking all kinds of risks, struggling ahead from dawn to dark. He slid across the tentative ice that the others dared not.

One time the sled broke through the ice, taking with it Dave and Buck. Both dogs nearly drowned and were half frozen by the time they were pulled out. They were coated solidly with ice, and the two men had to make them run around the fire to thaw them out. They ran so close to the fire that they were almost singed.

Another time, Spitz fell through, dragging the whole team along. But Buck strained backward with all his strength, his forepaws on the slippery edge and the ice breaking all around him. Dave also pulled backward with all his strength, as did Francois, but the ice broke before and behind them. There was no escape except up the cliff. Perrault, by some miracle,

The Call of the Wild

climbed up the cliff and threw a rope down and hoisted the dogs up one by one. Francois was the last to come out, sled and load. Miraculously they had survived.

By the time they had made it to the Hootalinqua and good ice, Buck was spent, as were the other dogs. But Perrault had yet to make up for the lost time and he pushed the dogs hard. The first day they covered around thirty-five miles to the Big Salmon; the next day thirty-five more to the Little Salmon; the third day forty miles, which brought them up toward the Five Fingers.

Buck's feet were not as compact and hard as the huskies'; generations as a domesticated dog had softened them. All day long he limped in agony. When camp was made, he could not move, not even getting up to eat his dinner although he was starving.

To make him feel better, each night after dinner Francois would rub the tops of

Buck's feet for half an hour. The dog-driver even sacrificed the tops of his moccasins to make four dog moccasins for Buck. This gave Buck so much relief that one morning when Francois forgot to put them on, Buck refused to budge. He lay on his back, his feet waving in the air, waiting for the moccasins to be put on. Even Perrault smiled at this. The well-worn footwear was thrown away only when Buck's feet had hardened to the trail.

As they were harnessing up one morning, Dolly, who was usually quite an inconspicuous dog, suddenly went mad. She let out a long, heartbreaking wolf howl that sent every dog bristling with fear. Without reason, she lunged straight toward Buck.

Buck was terrified, as he had never seen a dog go mad before, and he panicked. He raced away into the woods, with Dolly chasing after him. He ran across two

islands and was about to cross the main river in his desperation to get away from the crazed dog when he heard Francois calling out to him.

Putting all his faith into the dog driver, he stopped and gasped painfully for air, hoping that perhaps he would be saved. He saw that Francois had his ax held firmly in his hand and as he darted past him, he knew that the ax had crashed down upon Dolly.

Buck staggered onto the sled, exhausted and sobbing for air. Spitz saw that his nemesis was vulnerable and seized the opportunity. He sprang upon Buck and twice sank his teeth into his flesh, tearing the flesh to the bone. At that moment Francois's lash found Spitz. He then proceeded to administer the worst whipping Buck had ever seen any dog received before.

"He is a devil, that Spitz," said Perrault. "One day, he will kill Buck."

"But Buck is two devils," replied Francois. "I watch him all the time and I know that one day he'll go crazy and chew Spitz up and spit him out in the snow."

But from that day on, war was declared between Buck and Spitz.

CHAPTER 6

The Clash for Leadership

It was inevitable that the clash for leadership would come. Buck wanted it. His pride made him want it. Spitz, who was until then the lead dog and master of the team, felt his supremacy challenged and felt threatened. Buck was unlike any other Southland dog that Spitz had ever known. All the others had withered away, unable to take the toil of the trail, but Buck was masterful and matched Spitz in strength, savagery, and cunning. Buck was also gifted with the quality of patience,

71

which was nothing less than the primitive patience of the wild beasts of prey. His life and his experience with the man in the red sweater had also eliminated all rashness from his actions.

Buck also wanted this leadership. The desire was awakened by newfound instincts and his nature. Even though Buck's pride made him want the leadership, it was Spitz's pride that made him insecure of Buck.

Slowly but surely Buck began to challenge Spitz's leadership. He did this deliberately. One night, when it had snowed heavily, Pike, who regularly made mistakes, failed to appear. He was securely cocooned in his nest. Despite Francois's constant calls, he did not show up. Now, Spitz was blind with rage. He stomped across the camp, sniffing for Pike everywhere, growling so fiercely that Pike shivered with fear in his nest. Spitz finally unearthed Pike and was about to

administer a severe punishment when Buck angrily flew in between them and overthrew Spitz. Pike, encouraged by this mutiny, also joined in and sprang on the overthrown leader. It was Francois who caught wind of this and diffused the situation by whipping Buck. Pike, on the other hand, received his punishment from Spitz.

As they carried on their journey to Dawson, Buck continued to interfere with Spitz's authority. But he did this craftily, when Francois was not around. As a result of Buck's actions a general rebellion developed among the team. Things no longer went right, and there was constant bickering within the team. Dave and Sol-leks were unaffected, but the others went from bad to worse. Trouble was always around, and Francois knew that Buck was behind these acts of insubordination. But Buck was clever—after the whipping from Francois, he was sly and made sure he was never caught red-handed again.

Both Francois and Perrault knew that it was only a matter of time before there would be a clash when one of the two dogs would be sure to die. It was on more than one night that the sounds of scuffles between the dogs got Francois out of his tent fearful that Buck and Spitz were at each other.

But the opportunity did not present itself, and the team eventually made it to Dawson. Here there were many men and countless dogs, and Buck noticed they were all at work hauling cabin logs and firewood, doing the work that horses did in the Southland. All day they swung up and down the main street, their bells jingling, and at night the bells went silent.

Occasionally, Buck met a Southland dog, but they were the wild wolf-husky breed. Every night, regularly at nine, at twelve, and at three, they sang an eerie nocturnal song, and it delighted Buck so much that he joined in. The song of the huskies was an old song, as old as the breed itself. It was a sad song, filled with all the anguish of many generations.

These emotions stirred something in Buck, and when he sang and sobbed with

The Call of the Wild

the huskies, he cried for the pain of his existence, he cried for the pain that his ancestors had felt and for the fear and cold in their lives. The song of the huskies stirred so many emotions in Buck that he identified with his wild ancestors.

Seven days after they had pulled into Dawson, they decided to pull back toward Dyea and Salt Water. Perault had an extremely important dispatch to deliver. But more than that he had been gripped by travel pride. He wanted to make the record trip of the year. And the timing could not have been better. The dogs had been resting for a week and they were traveling light, as the police had organized to drop off food at one or two stops.

So the team set off trying to make their record trip.

While they achieved their daily targets, it was not without great trouble to Francois. Buck's mutiny was destroying the team's solidarity. It was no longer like one dog leaping through the traces. They no longer feared Spitz's leadership. Pike robbed him of half a piece of fish one evening, and another time, Joe and Dub fought Spitz and made him forgo their punishment. Even Billee was no longer as good-natured. Disorder ruled the camp. And although Dave and Sol-leks were unaffected, even they were becoming irritable, the misconduct affecting their ability to do their job. Francois stomped

about in anger, threw curses at everybody, and tore his hair out in frustration. His whip was working overtime, but it made no difference.

Buck's attitude toward Spitz had also turned tables—he now behaved like the bully, snarling menacingly at Spitz. The team was clearly divided: Out of fairness, Francois backed Spitz up with his whip, while Buck backed up the other dogs.

One night after dinner, at a campsite in Tahkeena, Dub spotted a snowshoe 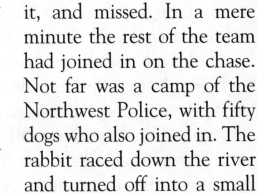 rabbit, made a grab for it, and missed. In a mere minute the rest of the team had joined in on the chase. Not far was a camp of the Northwest Police, with fifty dogs who also joined in. The rabbit raced down the river and turned off into a small creek. Buck led the pack of

sixty dogs around bend after bend, but the rabbit flashed on ahead.

Unknowingly, Spitz, cold and calculating, had broken away from the pack. He cut across a narrow path where the creek made a long bend. As Buck rounded the bend and spotted the rabbit before his eyes, just then he saw a sudden apparition cut the rabbit's path. Spitz grabbed the rabbit, and a loud cheer erupted from the pack at Buck's feet.

But Buck did not join in on the cheering. He was angry and, without a second thought, launched himself at Spitz and they rolled over in the powdery snow. In a flash both dogs knew that this was the big fight: Only one of them would survive.

Spitz quickly regained his composure and slashed Buck on the shoulder. As they circled around, snarling, watching for an advantage, the scene came back to Buck. It seemed not new or strange but was as if

this was how things were meant to be. His instincts had awakened.

Spitz was an experienced fighter. From Spitzbergen through the Arctic, and across Canada and the Barrens, he had held his own with all manner of dogs. He did not forget that his enemy was as angry and as instigated as he was. He never rushed in till he was prepared to face a rush, and would not attack until he had defended that attack.

Fang clashed fang, but Buck could not penetrate his enemy's guard. Buck tried in vain to sink his teeth into Spitz's neck, but failed each time as his fangs met Spitz's fangs. The fight was getting desperate. Time and time again Buck tried for the snow-white throat, where life bubbled near to the surface, and each and every time Spitz slashed him and got away.

Once Spitz knew that Buck was getting winded, he began his attack and started rushing into him. He repeatedly rushed toward his throat, but instead slammed his shoulder, overthrowing him. Buck went over, and the circle of dogs started to get up, believing the fight was finished. But Buck got up again, and the dogs sat down again. Buck wasn't going to give up without a tough fight.

Spitz was untouched while Buck

was panting hard, steaming with blood. Nothing moved, not even a leaf quivered. The circle of dogs watched expectantly, motionless and silent.

But Buck possessed a quality that made for greatness: imagination. He fought not only by instinct, but also with his head. He rushed at Spitz as if attempting the shoulder trick, but at the last moment swept low and closed in on Spitz's left foreleg. There was a crunching sound and Buck repeated the trick, injuring Spitz's right foreleg. Spitz struggled, but could not keep up. Buck showed no mercy.

The circle of dogs closed in so tight that Buck could feel the dogs breathing. Quivering and snarling, Spitz continued to stagger back and forth, as if to scare off death. He could see the tight circle of dogs, their gleaming eyes and lolling tongues. He had seen similar circles close in on his opponents before, only this time they seemed to be waiting to close in on him. But he knew that the fight was over.

Buck took one last lunge, and then, shoulder met shoulder. It was all over, and Spitz disappeared in the waiting circle of dogs. Buck stood and looked on—a new champion had emerged.

CHAPTER 7

The Leader of the Pack

The next morning when Perrault and Francois discovered that Buck was brutally wounded and bleeding and that Spitz was missing, they figured out exactly what had happened.

"That Spitz sure knows how to fight," Perrault said as he surveyed Buck's rips and cuts in the light of the fire.

"And Buck fights twice as hard," retorted Francois. But both men agreed that no more Spitz meant a lot less trouble.

Now that the fight was over and a

victor had emerged, the men wanted to get back to their record trip. Perrault packed up the camp and loaded the sled, and Francois began to harness the dogs. Buck trotted up to the front, assuming that he would now occupy the place that Spitz previously used to. But Francois, who did not notice him, brought the experienced Sol-leks to the front, believing he to be the best lead dog left in the team.

Francois slapped his thigh in

amusement. "Just look at Buck," he said. "He thinks that because he has killed Spitz so he deserves Spitz's job."

But Buck was not at all amused. He sprang up at Sol-leks in anger, driving him back, and stood in his place. Sol-leks was scared and quite willing to let go of the place in the front and go back to where he belonged.

"Go away, Buck," Francois said, still amused as he tried to shoo Buck away, but Buck refused to budge. Francois intended to stick to his decision and held Buck by the scruff and pushed him away. But when he turned his back, Buck had once again replaced Sol-leks.

By then, the dog driver was angry, and he picked up a club to try to "fix" Buck. Buck remembered the man in the red sweater had retreated slowly, so Buck did not attempt to charge in again. Instead he circled around, snarling with anger, watching the club so he could dodge it. After some time, Francois threw away the club thinking that Buck was escaping a thrashing. But Buck was now rebelling openly. He did not want to escape the thrashing, but he wanted the leadership. He had earned the leadership and would settle for no less.

Perrault also joined in to help Francois. Between the two men they ran around

Buck for the better part of an hour. They threw stones at him, they shouted curses at him. But it made no difference to Buck. He did not try to run away, just retreated around the camp, making his intentions clear. When his demand was met, he would return and all would be good.

Perrault looked at his watch and swore—they were already an hour late. Francois scratched his head—the men had to admit that they were beaten. The front was the only place in the sled for Buck. Francois went up to Sol-leks, unfastened his traces, and put him back to his own place. He called out to Buck, but he refused to go.

"Throw down your club," Perrault said to Francois.

As soon as Francois had thrown down his weapon, Buck trotted up triumphantly to what he knew was his rightful place. His traces were fastened, and both men

were along on their river trail.

While Francois had always valued Buck, he realized quickly that Buck was a natural-born leader. He took up his duties as leader competently—showing good judgment, quick thinking, and quick action. Buck proved to be an even better leader than Spitz, of whom Francois had

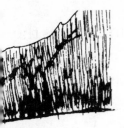

never seen an equal.

But it was at laying down the law and making his mates live up to it that Buck was really good. Dave and Solleks didn't seem particularly perturbed by the change in leadership. It was not their business; their job was to work hard at the traces. As long as it did not interfere with them, they did not care what happened. They didn't care if good-natured Billee took charge as long as he maintained order. The team had grown unruly in the last few days of Spitz's leadership, but Buck had licked them into shape. Pike, who pulled just behind Buck and who had never pulled more than an ounce against the breast band than he had to, received a proper shaking up for repeatedly loafing around. On Buck's first night in camp as the leader, he even managed to punish Joe, the sour one, something even Spitz had never managed to do. He simply overpowered him with his size until he ceased snapping and whimpered for mercy.

The general solidarity of the team improved, and once again the dogs leaped as one. Two more native huskies, Teek and Koona, were added to the team, and the manner in which Buck broke them in to the group took even Francois's breath away.

"Never have I seen a dog like Buck. He's worth a thousand dollars!" he said. Perrault agreed. The team was ahead of schedule and gaining each day. The trail was in excellent condition—there was no more snow to contend with, and it did not get colder.

The men rode and ran in turns, and the dogs were kept on the run with few stops. Even the Thirty-Mile River was relatively covered with ice, and they covered in one day what had taken them ten on the way coming in. In one run they made a sixty-mile dash; they ran so fast that the man whose turn it was to run had to tow behind the sled on a rope.

In the end, the team's effort paid off. It was a record run: Each day, for fourteen days, they'd averaged forty miles. Perrault and Francois were delighted. For three days they threw their chests up and down the main street of Skaguay and were swamped with invitations to celebrate. Buck had become a hero, and the team was the constant center of attraction for a crowd of dog busters and mushers.

After a few days, public attention turned to other idols. Then came the official orders: Francois and Perrault would be getting another team. Someone else would take charge of Buck's team. It had been a gradual friendship, and Francois

would miss Buck. He called Buck to him, put his arms around the dog, and cried. Buck would never see them again. Like the judge, then the man in the red sweater, Francois and Perrault, too, passed out of Buck's life. His time with the two men had been eventful. He had learned many skills, many instincts had been awakened, and he had become a leader. Now he was on to the next adventure of his life.

CHAPTER 8

Awakening Ancient Instincts

The team joined a company with a dozen of the other dog teams. Under the charge of a Scotch, all teams began their journey back to Dawson. For Buck's team, it was no longer about the glory of a record run, but hard labor ahead. They were now part of a mail train, carrying messages from the world to the men who had come to find gold under the shadow of the Pole.

Although Buck did not like this new job, again he accepted it with dignity. He made sure that the rest of his mates also

95

took pride in their work and did their fair share, just like Dave and Sol-leks, irrespective of whether or not they liked what they were doing.

Each day was much like the previous one. It was a monotonous life that passed with machine-like regularity. To the clock

each morning the cooks came out, built a fire, and breakfast was eaten. Each man had a task—some pitched the tents, others cut firewood, while some helped the cooks. Then before dawn some broke camp while others harnessed the dogs, and they were on their way. At night, camp was made again and the dogs were fed. After their fish was eaten, the dogs loafed about for an hour or so, sometimes playing, sometimes fighting. There were many fighters among the fifty-odd dogs in the camp, but battles with the fiercest had earned Buck a reputation, so when he growled and showed his teeth, they left him alone.

The Call of the Wild

For Buck, the best times were when he lay by the fire after a hard day's work. He often thought about his life—sometimes about Judge Miller, and his friends Toots and Ysabel, in the warm California sun.

But more often, he thought of the man in the red sweater, the death of his friend Curly, and the fight with Spitz. He was not homesick; the memories of the Southland had little power over him.

But more often, he thought of how Manuel the gardener had sold him at the station for a hundred dollars, the man in the red sweater, and the journey on the *Narwhal*. The memories of his friend Curly's death saddened him and haunted him at night. Often, he thought about the fight with Spitz. And sometimes he thought about the good things he had eaten and what he would like to eat.

More powerful, though, were the memories of his heredity, his instincts— which had been latent early in his life, but had come alive again. As he crouched by the fire, blinking at the dancing flames, it seemed they were the flames of some other fire. There crouched by that fire sat a man who looked different from the men he was used to seeing. This man was shorter, with longer arms. His muscles weren't rounded; instead, they were stringy and knotted. His body was covered with hair. This man uttered strange sounds and was afraid of the dark. He was a man from ancient times— a man who could not stand straight, but leaned forward on legs that were bent at the knees. His body seemed almost catlike, and he was always alert, as if he was afraid of things seen and unseen.

Beyond the fire, he saw in the distance the gleaming eyes of the great beasts of prey. He could hear the sounds they made as their bodies moved through the darkness. These dreams of another time made the hair on his back stand, and he would growl gently until the cook, sleeping by him, would shout for him to wake up. Then that other world would vanish and the real world would appear in front of his eyes.

The Call of the Wild

He would stretch and yawn and pretend to have awoken from his sleep.

It was a hard trip, with a heavy load behind them, which wore them out. To make matters worse, it snowed every day. The dogs were tired, and the drivers grumbled. By the time they got to Dawson, the dogs had become quite thin and needed a rest desperately. They should have been allowed at least ten days' rest when they got there, but just two days later they were on their way again, their sleds loaded with letters from the outside world.

Each night the dogs were tended to before the men ate. No man slept until he had looked at his dogs' feet. The drivers tried to make it as easy as possible for the dogs, but still, the dogs were exhausted.

The dogs became weaker day by day. Since the beginning of the winter they had traveled eighteen hundred miles. The distance was hard on even the toughest dogs. Buck was tired, but he maintained discipline and made his mates work fair. Billee cried even more than usual, Joe sulked even more than usual, and Sol-leks became completely unapproachable, blind side and otherwise.

Dave suffered the most. He became irritable and morose. He made his nest as soon as camp was pitched, and his driver had to feed him dinner there. He would often cry out with pain when the

sled jerked or strained suddenly. His case became a topic of interest for all the drivers and they would discuss it every night. One evening, they held an examination. Dave was brought out from his nest and they prodded and poked until the poor dog began to cry. They could not find any broken bones, but something seemed to be wrong inside. He became so weak that he kept falling in the traces.

The dog driver decided to remove him from the sled, giving Sol-leks his place. The driver's intention was to allow Dave a rest, but so strong was Dave's pride that he could not let any other dog do his work. Although he was unwell, he still had the pride of toil and trace and could not bear for any other dog to do his work.

When the sled started again, he began to run alongside slowly. He attacked Sol-leks repeatedly, all the while crying

The Call of the Wild

with pain and grief. The driver tried to push him away, even using his whip, but Dave resisted. He paid no heed to the lashes and the driver did not have the heart to strike him harder. He continued to run alongside the sled and then he fell, howling until the train of sleds had driven past. With the last ounce of his strength he managed to follow the sleds to their last stop, where he went and stood alongside Sol-leks. His driver had stopped to light his pipe from another driver and when the sleds began to set off again, he was surprised when his sled did not push off. Dave had bitten through Sol-leks's traces and was standing there in his old place. With his eyes he pleaded to remain there.

The driver called his mates to witness what had just happened. He was perplexed and saddened because he knew that a dog who was not allowed to do his job could die from a broken heart. He recalled instances in the past where dogs, too old for the work, or injured, had lost their will to live when cut out of their traces. Also, out of mercy they felt that if Dave was to die, he should die content in the traces. So he allowed Dave to pull the sled. Dave proudly pulled as before, but fell several times. He held on until they reached the camp for the night, limping all along on one of his hind legs. The driver made a place for him by the fire.

When it was time to leave in the morning, Dave crawled up to the dog driver. As the sled moved on, his friends saw that his strength had left him and he lay gasping in the snow, longing to go with them. They could hear him howl mournfully till they passed out of sight.

Suddenly the train halted. The dog driver walked back to the site where he had left Dave. The other men stopped talking. The sound of a revolver shot pierced the silence, and the man hurried back.

The whips snapped, the bells tinkled merrily, and the train continued on, but Buck knew and every other dog knew what had taken place behind the river trees.

CHAPTER 9

Living Out a Nightmare

Thirty days after the Salt Water Mail had left Dawson, they arrived in Skaguay, with Buck's team at the front. The dogs were completely worn out. Each of them had lost weight and was suffering from leg and shoulder injuries. Buck's 140 pounds had come down to 115. Pike, the malingerer, who had faked a hurt leg many times before, was truely limping, as Sol-leks and Dub had injured his shoulders.

When they arrived at Skaguay they

were clearly on their last leg. They could barely keep the traces tight, and on downward slopes just managed to keep out of the way of the sled.

They all had footsores, and none of them had any spring left in their feet, which made their journey harder. They had done twenty-five hundred miles over the winter, eighteen of which were covered with just five days' rest. Every inch of the team's strength was used up, and they did not have any reserves. Every muscle, every fiber, every cell was dead tired. The tiredness that they felt was not the one that comes through brief and excessive effort, but from the slow and prolonged drainage of strength.

The dog drivers promised them a much-deserved long rest. An interval of loafing and no work was required. But so many men had rushed to the Northland, and so many families, wives, and sweethearts had not, and the mail was taking on huge proportions. There was no time for a break. An official order declared that new Hudson Bay dogs were to be brought in and the old, tired dogs were to be disposed of. Dogs meant very little as compared to dollars, so they were to be sold.

The Call of the Wild

Only three days had passed when Buck and his mates realized how tired they really were. Then, on the fourth day, two Americans from the Southland came along and bought the team for a song. The men were called Charles and Hal. Charles was a middle-aged man with weak, watery eyes, and a mustache that twisted fiercely up, disguising a thin, limping lip underneath. Hal was a much younger man, not older than nineteen years, with a big Colt's revolver and a hunting knife strapped around him on a belt. Both men seemed completely out of place, and what they were doing there was a mystery to all.

When driven to their new camp, they saw a sorry state, everything was in disorder, the tent was half stretched, and the dishes were unwashed. They were introduced to the third member of their little party, a woman named Mercedes, who was Hal's older sister and Charles's wife.

The Call of the Wild

Buck watched apprehensively as they began to sloppily pack up the camp. As they bundled their entire luggage Buck discovered that while there was a great deal of effort in packing up, they had no method at all. The tent was rolled up three times larger than it should have been and the dishes were put away unwashed.

Three men from a neighboring camp watched on, grinning at one another.

"I should probably mind my own business, but I wouldn't carry such a heavy load if I were you, and I certainly wouldn't take the tent," said one.

"Undreamed of!" cried Mercedes, throwing up her hands in dainty dismay. "However in the world could I manage without a tent?"

"Because it's summer. You won't need it," the man replied, confirming what he already knew: This lot of people did not have a clue.

"I don't think the dogs will be able to pull it," said another.

"Why won't they?" demanded Charles.

"It just seems a bit top-heavy," replied the first man.

But Charles and Hal ignored these warnings and carried on, anyway. Hal took hold of the pole in one hand and whipped the lash with the other. "Mush on there," he ordered.

The dogs sprang up against the breast band and strained hard for a few moments and then relaxed, but they were unable to move the sled.

"The lazy brutes, I'll show them," shouted Hal, preparing to lash them.

"They're very weak," said one of the onlooking men. "They need a rest."

Hal whipped the dogs again, but the sled held as if it were an anchor. Hal began to whip the dogs again; when Mercedes

The Call of the Wild

interrupted, she held on to the whip. "Oh Hal, you mustn't do that," she squealed. "The poor dears. You must promise not to be harsh with them for the rest of the trip or I won't go another step," she said. She fell on her knees and put her arms around Buck and begged the dogs to pull hard. "What do you know about dogs?" Hal shouted back. "They're all lazy and need to be whipped to get them started. Ask anyone."

Another onlooker, who had been struggling hard to keep silent, finally spoke up. "I don't really care two hoots about you lot," he said. "It's the dogs I'm concerned about. The runners are frozen to the snow; you can help the dogs by breaking them."

A third attempt was made, taking his advice. The suggestion worked, and the sled forged ahead. They were on their way.

A hundred yards away, the path turned and sloped steeply onto the main road. Hal

did not have the experience to keep the top-heavy sled upright and as they swung around the bend, the sled toppled, spilling half its load. But the dogs, too angry at the treatment meted out to them and the unfair heavy load, did not stop.

Kindhearted citizens stopped to

collect the belongings. One suggested that they halve their load and add more dogs. Resentfully, Charles and Hal took the advice. As they began removing the extra weight, Mercedes cried at every item that was eliminated. After eliminating as much as they could, they were still

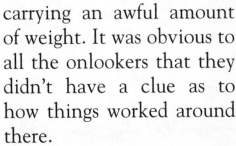

carrying an awful amount of weight. It was obvious to all the onlookers that they didn't have a clue as to how things worked around there.

So Charles and Hal went off and bought another six dogs. Of these, three were short-haired pointers, one was a Newfoundland, and the other two were mongrels. These newcomers knew nothing about pulling a sled. Buck and his mates quickly taught them their places and what not to do, but they could be taught what they needed to do. Soon, even the newcomers' spirits were broken by the ill treatment they received.

But Charles and Hal were very cheerful. They had never seen a sled pulled by fourteen dogs before and were convinced they were traveling in great

style. There was good reason why no sled in the Arctic was pulled by fourteen dogs: It was because one sled could not carry the food of fourteen dogs.

It was inevitable that they would run out of dog food. When the worn-out dogs pulled too slowly, Hal decided that the daily ration was not enough. He began to overfeed the dogs, not realizing that the dogs needed rest and not more food. Then Hal woke up one morning to the realization that more than half of his dog food was through and only a quarter of the distance covered. So he decided to reduce the rations and increase the days' travel.

The health of the dogs declined further. The first to go was Dub. His untreated shoulder injury went from bad to worse, and in the end, Hal was forced to use the gun on her. Six of the other dogs followed Dub.

By this time, Hal, Charles, and

Mercedes were also fighting incessantly. Stripped of its glamour and romance, the Arctic became a reality too harsh for them to accept.

Mercedes no longer considered the dogs but insisted on riding on the sled. She rode on it for days—the last straw for the

dogs. They fell in their traces and couldn't carry on any longer. Fed merely on strips of hide, gradually their bodies wasted away. They were bags of bones, in which sparks of life occasionally surfaced.

One day Billee fell and could not get up. Hal knocked him with an ax and

dragged his body to the side of the road. The next day, Koona suffered a similar fate. Buck staggered along at the head of the team, all the gloss paled from his beautiful coat, his frame cleanly outlined in his loose hide. It was heartbreaking, but Buck's heart was unbreakable.

From the fourteen dogs that started the journey, only five remained.

CHAPTER 10

Meeting John Thornton

It was beautiful spring weather, but neither man nor dog was aware of it.

Each day the sun rose earlier and set later—it was dawn by three in the morning and twilight at nine in the evening. Each day was awash with brilliant sunshine. The silence of winter had given way to the sounds of life awakening. Everything that had been dead in the winter began to thaw and live again. New saplings began to grow in the pines, the willows and aspens were bursting out in young buds, and shrubs and

125

vines were clothed in new shades of green. Crickets sang at night, and during the day all kinds of creepy-crawlies walked about. The forest was bursting with the sounds of partridges and woodpeckers booming and knocking, squirrels chattering, birds singing, and wild fowl honking—nature's orchestra was in full form.

The ice and the snow had started to melt, and water trickled down from every hill. Everything was thawing. The sun shone on the Yukon River and it strained to break loose the ice that bound it down. Airholes formed, and thin sections of ice fell through the river. And amid all this activity staggered the two men, the woman, and the huskies.

Of the five dogs that remained, Joe was too exhausted to be spiteful and Pike was only half conscious and couldn't be bothered to malinger. Only Sol-leks was still faithful to the trail but he was disappointed that he didn't have enough strength to do his job properly. Teek had traveled the least of the dogs and had beaten the most because he was the freshest of all. Buck was still the lead, but no longer enforced any discipline, and was almost blind with weakness; he kept to the trail merely by feel of it under his feet.

With falling dogs and a weeping Mercedes riding on the sled, the team staggered into John Thornton's camp at the mouth of the White River. Mercedes dried her tears, Hal cursed constantly, and Charles sat down stiffly to have a rest. When the sled stopped, the dogs collapsed as if they were dead.

John Thornton was putting the final touches to an ax that he had made from a piece of birch. He carried on with his work as Charles talked. He listened while he continued to work, giving occasional monosyllabic replies. When asked, he offered brief, curt advice. He had dealt with people like these and knew that advice would fall upon deaf ears. But, still, he warned the party not to take any chances on the melting ice and not to go any farther.

"They also told us that we wouldn't get to the White River, but here we are," Hal said with a sneer, in response to Thornton's warning.

"And they were right," Thornton answered. "The bottom's likely to drop out at any moment. Only fools, with the blind luck of fools, could have made it. I wouldn't risk it for all the gold in Alaska."

"That's because you're not a fool, I suppose," said Hal. "Anyway, we're carrying on to Dawson."

Preparing to leave, Hal uncoiled his whip and lashed it at Buck. Thornton continued his work on the ax, knowing fully well that it was senseless to get between a fool and his foolishness.

But the team did not get up at Hal's command. They had long reached the stage where blows were required to bring them to their feet. In an effort to get them to move, Hal mercilessly whipped his tired troops. Thornton, although annoyed, did not say anything. Sol-leks was the first to crawl to his feet, followed by Teek. Joe yelped with pain while Pike fell twice and managed to rise up on his third attempt. Buck, though, did not make an effort at all. He lay quietly where he had fallen. The lash bit into him time and again, but he neither whined nor struggled.

A spectator to this horrific scene, Thornton's eyes moistened and he decided to say something, but he changed his mind. As the whipping continued, he got up and began to pace hesitantly.

This was the first time Buck had failed, and it drove Hal into a mad rage. He exchanged the whip for a club. But Buck refused to move even under the heavier blows. He had made up his mind not to get up. A vague sense of impending doom had taken over him when they pulled into the bank. He sensed disaster was close when he had felt the thin ice under his feet all day. And disaster was where Hal seemed to be taking the team.

As the blows continued, Buck felt numb. It felt as though he were watching himself from a distance, aware that he was being beaten. The last sensations of pain left him. It was no longer his body, it seemed so far away.

And then, suddenly, without warning, uttering an animal-like cry, Thornton sprang upon Hal. Mercedes screamed as Hal fell back as if he were hit by a tree. Charles looked on but was unable to get up because of the stiffness in his body. Thornton stood over Buck, struggling to control himself, too angry to speak.

"If you strike that dog again and again, I'll kill you," he said at last, choking on his words.

"It's my dog," Hal replied, wiping the blood from his mouth. "Get out of my way, or I'll fix you. I'm going to Dawson."

But Thornton had no intention of

getting out of the way, and continued to stand between Hal and the dog. As Hal drew his long hunting knife, Mercedes became hysterical. Thornton rapped Hal's knuckles with the ax handle, knocking the knife to the ground, and rapped again as he tried to pick it up. Then he picked it

up himself and cut Buck's traces.

Hal had no fight left in him. Besides, his hands were full with his hysterical sister and Buck was too near dead to be of any use. Minutes later the limping dogs pulled the sled out from the bank and down the river. Buck watched them go; Pike was leading, Sol-leks was at the wheel, and Joe and Teek were in between. They were limping along, with Mercedes still insisting upon sitting on the sled. Hal guided the gee-pole, and Charles stumbled along behind. Thornton knelt beside him and searched for broken bones. Luckily, Buck had survived with little more than nasty bruises and terrible starvation.

They watched the sled, which was by now a mile away, and saw the dogs and men crawling along the thin ice. Then suddenly, they saw the sled's back end drop down, and also the gee-pole with Hal clinging to it. Mercedes screamed, and Charles turned to run back. Then the ice gave way, and the dogs and men disappeared. All they could see was a big gaping hole. The bottom had dropped out of the trail.

Hal and Charles had been warned, but they had chosen to ignore it. Nature had her own rules—they found out the hard way.

John Thornton and Buck looked at each other.

"You poor devil," said Thornton, and Buck licked his hand.

CHAPTER 11

The Love of a Man

The previous December John Thornton's legs had frozen, and Pete and Hans had left him at camp to recover. Hans and Pete had gone to secure a saw-log raft that would take them all to Dawson. Thornton was still limping slightly when he rescued Buck, but the continued warm weather got rid of the limp.

Lying by the White River, watching the running water and listening to the hum of nature and the songs of the humming birds, Buck began to regain his strength. His wounds healed, his muscles grew, and flesh covered his bones once again. The rest was certainly well deserved, considering that Buck had traveled three thousand miles. Buck enjoyed this loafing about, especially as he had made very good friends that spring. They all loafed together—John Thornton, Buck, and Thornton's other two dogs, Skeet, a little Irish setter, and Nig, a big black dog that was half bloodhound and half deerhound.

The Call of the Wild

Skeet was the first to make friendly advances toward Buck, who, in his wounded condition, was unable to resist. Skeet had the doctor's instincts and she tended to Buck like a cat tends to kittens. Every morning after breakfast she washed and cleansed Buck's wounds until he came to look forward to them as much as he did Thornton's help. Nig was equally friendly, but not as demonstrative. As they waited for Hans and Pete to bring them the raft that would take them to Dawson, they developed a happy friendship, playing all sorts of silly games; in this way, Buck recovered and happily skipped into his new life.

To Buck's surprise, neither Skeet nor Nig showed any jealousy toward him, but were happy to share Thornton's kindness. It was for the first time that Buck experienced genuine passionate love, the kind he had never before seen in his life, not even in

Northern California. With the judge's sons, hunting and tramping had been a working partnership; with the judge's grandsons, a sort of pompous guardianship; and even with the judge he had shared a sort of stately and dignified friendship. But it had taken John Thornton to arouse in Buck a love that was so intense.

Not only did Buck owe Thornton his life, but he was also the ideal master. Many men look after their dogs with a sense of duty, but Thornton looked after his dogs as if they were his children, always remembering to offer a cheerful word and enjoying long chats with them.

Buck especially loved the way Thornton took his head roughly between his hands and rested his own head upon Buck, and how he shook him back and forth, calling him funny names.

When released, Buck sprang to his feet, his mouth almost laughing, his eyes

The Call of the Wild

doing the talking as his throat vibrated with unuttered sound; and like that, he would remain. John Thornton understood what this meant. "God! You can all but speak!" he would say to Buck.

Even Buck had his own expression of love for Thornton. He would seize Thornton's hand in his mouth and close it so fiercely that the flesh bore the impression of his teeth for some time after. But Thornton understood that this feigned bite was actually a caress.

For the most part, however, Buck's love was expressed in adoration. While he went wild with happiness when Thornton spoke to him, he did not seek these tokens. Unlike Skeet, who would nudge Thornton until he responded, or Nig, who would rest his head on Thornton's knee, Buck was content to adore him at a distance. He would lie at Thornton's feet by the hour, eager, alert, just watching him. The communication between man and dog was such that sometimes the strength of Buck's gaze would draw Thornton's face toward him to return the gaze.

For a long time after his rescue, Buck did not want Thornton out of his sight. Since he had arrived in the Northland, he had had no permanent masters. He was afraid that, like the judge, Perrault, and Francois, Thornton would also pass out of his life forever. This fear even pervaded Buck's sleep. Worried, he would then shake off sleep and creep through the cold to the flap of the tent, where he would stand and listen to the sound of his master's breathing.

In spite of this great love he had for Thornton, which seemed to return Buck's civilizing tendencies, the primitive instincts that the Northland had aroused in him remained alive. Faithfulness and devotion, things born of domestication, were in him; yet he retained his wildness. He was now no longer the soft Southland dog stamped with generations of domestication; he was more like a thing of the wild who had come to sit by Thornton's fire. He would not steal from Thornton because of his great love for the man, but from any other man in any other camp, he would not hesitate to steal.

He had learned the law of fang and club, and it had made him merciless. His face was marked by the teeth of many dogs, and he had fought fiercely and shrewdly. He would never draw back from a foe even though it might lead to death—this he had learned from Spitz and from the chief fighting dogs of the police and the mail, and he knew there was no middle course. He would never pick a fight with Skeet or Nig—they were much too good-natured— but he clearly informed all other dogs of his supremacy. Kill or be killed, eat or be eaten—that was the law that had existed since time immemorial, and this was the law he obeyed.

Buck was much older than the days he had seen. He linked the past with the present. He sat by Thornton's fire, a broad-breasted dog, white-fanged and long-furred; but behind that were all kinds of dogs, half wolves and wild wolves, urgent and prompting. They tasted the meat he ate and the water he drank. They scented the wind with him; they listened with him and told him the sounds made by the wild in the forests. They directed his actions, dreamed with him, and became themselves the stuff of his dreams.

So strong was the call of these ancient dogs that each day mankind slipped farther away from Buck. Often he heard a call from the forest, thrilling and alluring, and he felt compelled to turn his back on the fire and run into the forest. He did not know why or where and did not question why or where from the depths of the forest this call sounded. But each time, his love for John Thornton drew him back to the fire again.

But it was only Thornton; the rest of mankind meant nothing to him. When Thornton's partners, Hans and Pete, arrived, Buck refused to acknowledge

them until he learned that they were close to Thornton. Even then, he only tolerated them passively, accepting favors from them as if he were doing them a favor. But they were men similar to Thornton and they understood Buck and his ways and did not insist upon an intimacy.

For Thornton, however, his love only seemed to grow. Buck would do anything

for him. One day, on their way to the head-waters of the Tanana, the men and dogs were sitting on the crest of a cliff, which fell straight down to naked bedrock three hundred feet below. Thornton was sitting near the edge, and a silly experiment crossed his mind: "Jump, Buck!" he commanded, sweeping his arm out and over the chasm. He wanted to know what the dog's reaction would be.

He got his answer soon enough, as the very next instant he was grappling with Buck on the extreme edge while Hans and Pete dragged them back to safety.

"It's uncanny," Pete said, after it was all over and they had caught their breath.

Thornton shook his head. "Splendid as it is, it is terrible, too, and sometimes it scares me," he said.

"I'm not going to be around the man who lays a hand on you when this one's around," Pete announced conclusively, nodding his head toward Buck.

"Me neither," agreed Hans.

And it was soon, before the end of the year, in Circle City that Pete's fears were accurately realized.

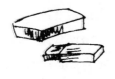

CHAPTER 12

Buck the Hero

It was in a bar in Circle City later that year that Buck proved just how protective he was about Thornton.

A bad-tempered man called "Black" Burton had picked a fight with a man and Thornton had good-naturedly stepped in to diffuse it. As always, lying in a corner with his head on his paws, Buck was watching his master's every move.

Then, without warning, Burton struck Thornton, sending him spinning against the bar. What happened next became legend across every camp in Alaska: Buck roared and flew through the air and lunged for Burton's throat; Burton threw up his hand in defense, but was hurled to the floor with Buck on top of him. Buck loosened his teeth from the flesh of the man's arm and drove in again and went straight for his throat. This time the man could not defend himself properly and Buck seriously injured the man.

Then the crowd was upon Buck, and he was driven off; but while a surgeon

checked the bleeding, he prowled up and down, growling furiously, attempting to rush in, and being forced back by an array of hostile clubs.

A "miners' meeting," called on the spot, decided that the dog had sufficient provocation, and Buck was discharged. But his reputation was made, and from that day his name spread through every camp in Alaska.

In the fall of that year, Buck saved Thornton's life yet again. Pete, Hans, and Thornton were lining a long and narrow poling boat down a bad stretch of rapids on the Forty-Mile Creek. Hans and Pete moved along the bank with a thin Manila rope from tree to tree, while Thornton remained in the boat, helping its descent by means of a pole, and shouting directions to the shore. Buck, on the bank, worried and anxious, kept abreast of the boat, his eyes never off his master.

At a particularly bad spot, an accident flung. Thornton was thrown far out of the boat and he was carried downstream toward the worst part of the rapids, a stretch of wild water in which no swimmer, however good, could survive.

Buck had sprung in on the instant; and amid a mad swirl of water, he overhauled Thornton. When he felt him grasp his

tail, Buck headed for the bank, swimming with all his strength. But below was the fatal roaring where the wild current went wilder. The swim toward the shore was hard and the pull downward was fast. Thornton was sure that the shore was impossible. He scraped furiously over a rock, clutching it with both hands, releasing Buck. Above the roar of the churning water he shouted, "Go, Buck! Go!"

Buck was swept downstream, but when he heard Thornton's command repeated, he partly reared out of the water and turned obediently toward the bank. He swam powerfully and was dragged ashore by Pete and Hans at the very point where swimming ceased to be possible and destruction began.

They knew that the time a man could cling to a slippery rock was for only a matter of minutes, and they ran as fast as they could up the bank to a point far above where Thornton was hanging on. They attached the line with which they had been snubbing the boat to Buck's neck and shoulders, taking care that it would not strangle him, and launched him into the stream. Buck jumped off boldly, but he missed his target completely. Hans and Pete had to drag him out of the water and pump the water out of him. They heard Thornton's weak cry, and although they could not make out the word, they knew that it was a desperate call for help. His master's voice was like an electric shock for Buck, and he jumped up and ran to the bank of the river. Buck was not concerned about his own life. Thornton was in danger, and he needed to help him. He was ready for another try.

After one failed attempt where he nearly drowned, Buck found his target and Thornton saw him coming toward him like a battered ram, and held on to his shaggy neck with both arms. Strangling and suffocating, sometimes one on top of the other, they made it. Hans pulled the rope and dragged the two onto the bank. Buck had saved Thornton's life.

Thornton was himself bruised and battered, but his first glance was toward Buck's limp and lifeless body. Nig had started howling, and Skeet was licking Buck's wet face. First Thornton carefully checked Buck's body. Buck had broken three ribs during the dramatic rescue. Thornton would not leave until Buck's ribs had healed and camp was laid there until Buck was fit to travel again.

Later that winter, at Dawson, Buck performed another exploit—not as heroic as saving a life, but one that put his name many notches higher on the totem pole of Alaskan fame. It all began with a conversation in the Eldorado Saloon, in which men were boasting about their dogs.

Buck, because of his record, was the target for these men, and Thornton was driven to defend him. One man bragged that his dog could start a sled with a load of five hundred pounds and walk off with it, and another raised this amount to six hundred for his dog.

Thornton, carried away by the talk in the bar, declared that Buck could start with a thousand pounds.

Matthewson, a Bonanza king, was amazed. "Can he really?" he asked.

Thornton coolly affirmed his claim, adding that not only could Buck start it, but he could also walk one hundred yards with it.

"Well," Matthewson said, slowly and deliberately, for all to hear, "I bet you one thousand dollars that says he can't. And here it is." He slammed a sack of gold dust down on the bar.

Nobody spoke. Thornton's bluff, if bluff it was, had been called. He felt a flush of warm blood creep up his face. The truth was that he did not know whether Buck could start a thousand pounds. Half a ton! Suddenly the enormousness of the claim appalled him. He had great faith in Buck's strength and had often thought him capable of starting such a load; but never, until now, had he faced the possibility of it—and in front of so many witnesses, too. Also, he did not have a thousand dollars; nor did Hans or Pete.

"I have a sled standing outside now, with twenty fifty-pound sacks of flour on it," Matthewson went on with brutal directness. "So let's try it."

Thornton borrowed the money from an old comrade and put his money where his mouth was. The bar quickly emptied as the men streamed outside to see this great challenge. Word spread like fire, and soon several hundred men gathered around the sled, and gamekeepers began to lay odds on the outcome of the wager.

Matthewson's sled, loaded with a thousand pounds of flour, had been standing for a couple of hours, and in the intense cold (it was sixty below zero) the runners had frozen to the hard-packed snow. The odds of the wager went up to

three to one against Buck. There were no takers. Not one man believed him capable of the feat.

Thornton's doubt was strong in his face, but his fighting spirit was aroused—the fighting spirit that soars above odds and fails to recognize the impossible.

Buck, with his own harness, was put into the sled. He could sense the excitement and felt that in some way he must do a great thing for John Thornton. Men marveled at his appearance, they felt his muscles and proclaimed them hard as iron, and the odds went down to two to one. One man from a wealthy family was so impressed by Buck that he offered to buy him from Thornton for eight hundred dollars.

Thornton stepped to Buck's side. He took his head in his hands and rested cheek on cheek. He did not playfully shake him, or murmur soft love curses. "As you love me, Buck," he whispered in his ear. Buck whined with eagerness. He seized Thornton's hand between his jaws, pressing in with his teeth and releasing it slowly, half reluctantly. It was his answer.

"Now Buck," said Thornton. At Thornton's command, Buck threw himself forward, tightening the traces with a jarring lunge. The sled swayed and trembled and half started forward. One of his feet slipped, and a man groaned aloud. Then the sled lurched ahead in a rapid succession of jerks, which diminished as the sled gained momentum and moved steadily along.

The crowd looked on, breathless and in disbelief.

Thornton ran behind Buck, shouting encouraging words. As he neared the pile of firewood that marked the end of the hundred yards, a cheer began to grow, which burst into a roar as he passed the firewood and halted at command. Hats and mittens were thrown up in the air, and even Matthewson looked impressed.

The man who had offered eight hundred dollars for Buck ran back to Thornton. He had increased his offer—now he was willing to buy him for one thousand dollars, and even one thousand two hundred dollars.

But Thornton fell on his knees beside Buck, the tears streaming down his face. Buck seized his hand in his teeth. Thornton shook him back and forth. The onlookers stepped back in respect and were silent in admiration of this amazing pair and the incredible feat.

CHAPTER 13

The Forest Beckons

With the sixteen hundred dollars Buck earned Thornton in the wager, he was able to pay off debts and make plans for the future. Thornton, Hans, and Pete decided to journey to the East in search of the legendary Lost Cabin mine, believed to contain gold unlike any known in the Northland.

This mine was steeped in tragedy and mystery. Many men had tried to look for this fabled mine, but not many had found it and none had returned from it to tell the tale. No living man had looted this

treasure house before, and the three men and their dogs set off to achieve what other men had failed to do.

Thornton was a man who made few demands on both man and nature. Unafraid of the wild, he could survive with just his rifle and a handful of salt. Tools and ammunition made up for most of the load on the journey, and the men hunted their food along the way. The men were unrushed and patient, and had set no time limit for their journey.

The Call of the Wild

To Buck it was a journey of endless delights. He loved the hunting and the fishing and the wandering to strange unknown places. The group wandered for months on end. They would camp here and there, the dogs loafing about and the men burning holes through the frozen muck and gravel and washing countless pans of dirt by the heat of the fire hoping

to discover the yellow metal so desired by man. Sometimes they went hungry, sometimes they feasted, all depending upon the availability of prey and the luck they had with the hunt. The little party was in no hurry, so if they did not find meat, they would carry on traveling confident that sooner or later, they would find it.

Seasons came and went and they continued on through uncharted territory. In the summer, they rafted across blue mountain lakes and picked strawberries and flowers as luscious as those in the Southland. In the fall they came up on a sad and silent lake country, where there was no sign of life, only the blowing of cold winds, the forming of ice,

and the melancholy rippling of waves on lonely beaches.

As another winter came, they stumbled on the trampled trails of men who had gone before them. Spring came once more, and at last they reached the end of their wandering. They did not find the Lost Cabin, but were face-to-face with

a shallow place where the gold gleamed like yellow butter.

Each day that the men worked they earned thousands of dollars in clean dust and nuggets, which was sacked in moose-hide bags, fifty pounds to the bag. These bags were then piled up outside the cabin like firewood. Day after day they worked like beasts. While they toiled, there was little for the dogs to do but occasionally haul in the meat that the men hunted. Buck spent long hours lying by the fire. The visions of the ancient, short-legged man came more often now, and Buck found himself wandering with him to the other world that he remembered.

Fear had dominated this world. He watched the hairy man sleeping restlessly by the fire, waking many times, always on the alert for hidden danger. They walked along the beach gathering shellfish to eat. They crept through the forest, their eyes set on the lookout for danger and their legs prepared to run like the wind as it appeared. Buck kept close to the hairy man's heels; alert and vigilant were the pair of them, for the man heard and smelled as keenly as Buck. This hairy man could climb trees and seemed as comfortable on them as he did on the ground, and Buck had memories of keeping vigil as the man slept in a tree, holding tightly.

And close to the visions of the ancient man was the calling of a sound from the depth of the forest. The sound filled him with great unrest and strange desires. He felt a vague happiness, but could not understand what the yearning was for. Sometimes he followed the call into the forest. There he would crouch for hours behind the fungus-covered trunks of fallen trees, wide-eyed and wide-eared. He would stick his nose into the cool soil and snort with joy at the smell of the earth.

Often, he would be lying in camp, dozing lazily in the heat of the day, when suddenly he would lift up his head and cock up his ears, intent and listening, then he would spring to his feet and dash away, and on and on, for hours, through the forest and across the open spaces. He loved to run down dry watercourses, and to spy upon the bird life in the woods. He could lie down for a whole day, just watching the partridges strut up and down.

The Call of the Wild

Most of all, he loved to run about the forest on summer nights, listening to the sleepy sounds of the forest, reading signs and sounds like men read books, all the time hoping to find the mysterious thing that called to him.

One night he woke from his sleep with a start. From the forest came the call, but it was like never before. It was like a howl, but unlike any made by a husky dog. But to Buck it was like a familiar sound, one that he had heard before.

He sprang through the sleeping camp swiftly and silently, slowing down as he came closer to the sound. Then he saw it—standing, with nose pointing to the sky, a long and lean timber wolf.

He made no noise, but the wolf sensed Buck's presence and it stopped howling. He fled as soon as he saw Buck. Buck followed, and tried to overtake him. They reached a dead-end and the wolf turned

around, snarling and snapping. But Buck did not want to attack him. Instead, he circled around, making friendly advances. But the wolf was still suspicious and the chase continued. Buck was thrice the size of the wolf and the wolf was afraid. But Buck's persistence paid off. Finally, the wolf realized that Buck meant no harm, so he stopped and sniffed noses with him.

For a while they played together, and then the wolf made it clear that he was going somewhere and that Buck could go with him. Together they ran for hours and hours in the twilight until daylight came.

As Buck ran side by side with his brother from the woods in the place where the call came from, he was extremely happy. He knew he was at last answering the call. Memories came flooding back —he had done this before, somewhere in that other and dimly remembered world, and he was doing it again, running free in the open, with the soil under his feet and the wide sky overhead.

When they had stopped by a running stream for drinking water, Buck remembered John Thornton and sat down. The wolf started to run toward the place where the sound was coming from. When he saw that Buck was hesitant, he nudged him in encouragement. But Buck turned about

and started to walk away slowly. He had to get back to Thornton.

For the better part of an hour the wild brother followed him, whining softly. Then he sat down, pointed his nose upward, and howled. It was a mournful howl, and as Buck held steadily on his way he heard it grow faint and fainter until it was lost in the distance.

When Buck returned to the camp, Thornton was eating dinner. He jumped up on him in a frenzy of affection and love, licking his face. Thornton was equally delighted to see him, and returned the embrace fondly.

For two days Buck did not let Thornton out of his sight. But then the call became stronger and Buck's restlessness increased. He began to roam the woods again, staying away from camp for days. But his wild brother did not return. He began hunting for his food, fishing for salmon in a stream. One time he hunted down a large black bear, the hard fight arousing the last of Buck's latent ferocity. The men saw him leave the camp, but did not see the terrible transformation that took place when he entered the forest.

Buck had already dragged down a bear, but he wished to beat a larger and stronger beast. His opportunity came when he saw a band of moose at the head of the creek. The chief was a great bull, who stood over six feet from the ground. For half a day Buck stalked his victim, attacking from all sides. Finally, the herd gave up its support of the old bull. He had lived a long, strong life, full of fight and struggle, and now he faced his end at the teeth of a creature whose head did not even reach beyond his knees. From then on, Buck did not leave his prey for even a moment. At last, at the end of the fourth day, Buck pulled the great moose down.

For a day and a night he stayed close to the kill, eating and sleeping in turn. Then, refreshed and rested, he made his way back to Thornton. But as he proceeded back to the camp, he could not shake off the feeling that a calamity was to occur.

CHAPTER 14

The Call of the Wild

Buck sprinted back home, running for hour after hour, through strange parts of the forest, so sure of his way back that it would put a man and his compass to shame. He stopped a few times to breathe in the morning air but read a message that made him run even faster. Every nerve in his body was tense and alert.

The forest was strangely silent; the birds had stopped calling and the squirrels had disappeared. As he glided slowly along, his nose was jerked with a strong force. Suddenly, he picked up a fresh scent and followed it to a thicket. There he found Nig, lying on his side, dead, arrows protruding from both sides of his body.

A hundred yards farther on, Buck came upon one of the sled dogs Thornton had bought in Dawson, thrashing about, struggling to stay alive. But Buck passed him without stopping. He could hear the faint sound of singing from the camp as he ran toward it. At the edge of a clearing he saw Hans, lying on his face, no longer alive, arrows sticking out from his back.

It was what he saw next that sent Buck flying into rage. A group of Yeehat Indians were dancing about the destroyed lodge. They seemed to be responsible for all the chaos and carnage. Buck's passion and love for Thornton took over all sense of reason and he lost his head. With a loud roar, Buck hurled himself upon them. First he sprang at the chief of the Yeehats and ripped open his throat. Like a hurricane

he ripped in passing, not worrying about the victim, moving on to the throat of a second man.

There was no stopping Buck. He charged at them, defying the arrows they shot at him. So fast were his movements and so close were the Indians tangled together that they shot arrows at one another. One young hunter hurled a spear in Buck's direction and missed completely, the spear piercing through the chest of another Indian. Then panic seized the Yeehats, and they fled in terror into the woods, shouting that the Evil Spirit had come.

In his rage, Buck was no different from the devil. He followed them into the trees and dragged them down like deer. So scared were the Yeehat Indians that they scattered far and wide and it was almost a week until they met and counted their losses. Then, tired of the pursuit, Buck returned to the camp. There he found Pete, who was also dead, still covered with his blankets, the surprise clear on his face. Buck then picked up the scent of Thornton's desperate struggle and followed it to a deep pool.

By the edge of the pool he found Skeet, faithful to Thornton to the very end. But the pool was muddy and hid what it contained. But Buck knew that it contained John Thornton and that he was dead.

The Call of the Wild

All day Buck brooded by the pool or roamed restlessly about the camp. John Thornton's death left a big void in Buck; he could not understand it. It felt like hunger, but it ached and ached.

When he sniffed the bodies of the Indians—he felt vindicated. But in his grief he also became aware of a great pride in himself: He had killed men. He told himself that he would no longer be afraid of men, except when they held arrows, spears, and clubs.

Night fell, and a full moon rose high over the trees into the sky, lighting the land till it lay bathed in ghostly day. And with the coming of the night, brooding and mourning by the pool, Buck became alive to a stirring of the new life. He became aware of sounds in the forest that weren't the sounds made by the Yeehat Indians. In the distance, Buck heard a faint sharp yelp, followed by a chorus

of similar sharp yelps. As the moments passed, the yelps grew closer and louder. Again Buck recognized them as the sounds from the other world of his memory. It was the call—stronger than ever before. He walked to the center of the open space and listened. And as never before, he was ready to obey. Now that John Thornton was no more, Buck's last tie to mankind was broken. Man and the claims of man no longer bound him.

Hunting their meat just as the Yeehats were hunting, a pack of wolves crossed the streams following the migrating moose and entered Buck's valley and he stood waiting for them. Into the clearing where the moonlight shone they poured in, and in the center of it all was Buck.

When they saw Buck, large and motionless, the wolves were awed and the boldest one in the pack sprang for him.

But Buck quickly overpowered him and broke his neck. There he stood, just as motionless as before, as the wolf rolled in pain on the ground. Three others tried, but were punished, their shoulders and throats bleeding.

This was sufficient to fling the whole pack forward, pell-mell, crowded together, blocked and confused by its eagerness to pull down the prey. Buck's marvelous quickness and agility stood him in good stead. Pivoting on his hind legs and snapping and snarling, he was everywhere at once, presenting a front that was apparently unbroken, so swiftly did he whirl and guard from side to side. But to prevent them from getting behind him, he was forced back down past the pool and into the creek bed till he came up against a high gravel bank. He worked along to a right angle in the bank, which the men had made in the course of mining, and in this angle he came to the bay, protected on three sides and with nothing to do but face the front.

And so well did he face it that at the end of half an hour the wolves drew back discomfited. The tongues of all were out and lolling, the white fangs showing cruelly white in the moonlight. Some were lying down with heads raised and ears pricked forward; others stood on their feet watching him; and still others were lapping water from the pool.

One wolf, long and lean and gray, advanced cautiously in a friendly manner, and Buck recognized the wild brother with whom he had run for a night and a day. He whined softly and Buck whined back and then they sniffed noses. An old wolf also came forward in friendship. Then he sat down, nose pointing to the moon, and broke out the long wolf howl. The others followed his lead.

The Call of the Wild

The Call of the Wild

Now the call came to Buck in unmistakable accents. Buck, too, sat down and howled for a while. This time it came easily to him. The pack crowded around him, sniffing in a half-friendly and a half-savage manner. The leaders soon sprang away into the woods with the others following. The wolves swung in behind, yelping in chorus and Buck ran with them, side by side with his wild brother, yelping as he ran.

It would be a mistake to assume that Buck's story ends there.

It was not long before the Yeehats noticed a change in the appearance of the timber wolves.

Some of the timber wolves were seen with splashes of brown on the head and muzzle, while others with a splash of white down the chest.

But more remarkable is a story passed

down by the Yeehats. They tell of a Ghost Dog that runs at the head of the pack. They are very much afraid of this dog, as he is more cunning than they are. He steals from them in cold winters, robs their traps, and kills their dogs. They tell of terrible stories. Such is their fear that each fall, when the Yeehats follow the movements of the moose, there is one valley they dare not enter. And when women are told how the spirit came to choose this valley as an abiding place, they become sad.

The tale grows worse. There are hunters who fail to return to the camp, and others who find their comrades with their throats ripped, with wolf prints all over the snow.

In the summers there is one visitor to that valley of which the Yeehats do not know. It is a great, gloriously coated wolf, like, and yet unlike, all other wolves. He crosses alone from the smiling timber land and comes down into an open space among the trees.

Here, a yellow stream flows from rotted moose-hide sacks and sinks into the ground, with long grass growing through, hiding its yellow from the sun.

There he waits for some time, howling once, long and mournfully, and then leaves.

But he is not always alone. When the long winter nights come on and the wolves hunt in the valley, he is seen running at the head of the pack. He leaps higher than his mates and sings a song of the younger world, which is the song of the pack.

About the Author

Jack London was born in 1876 and was one of the most successful American writers of the early twentieth century.

Jack grew up in the poverty-stricken slums of Oakland, California, and at the age of seventeen set sail on a ship to be part of the Klondike gold rush that was to become a part of his well-received novel *The Call of the Wild*. His other popular books include *White Fang* and *The Sea Wolf*, the latter is often considered to be his best novel.

Largely self-taught, London was one of the first Americans to make a career from writing stories.

The Adventures of Tom Sawyer
The Adventures of Pinocchio
Alice in Wonderland
Anne of Green Gables
Beauty and the Beast
Black Beauty
The Call of the Wild
A Christmas Carol
Frankenstein
Great Expectations
Journey to the Center of the Earth
The Jungle Book
King Arthur and the Knights of the Round Table
Little Women
Moby Dick
The Night Before Christmas and Other Holiday Tales
Oliver Twist
Peter Pan
The Prince and the Pauper
Pygmalion
The Secret Garden
The Time Machine
Treasure Island
White Fang
The Wind in the Willows
The Wizard of Oz